THIS IS ME!

CREATIVE VOICES

Edited By Jenni Harrison

First published in Great Britain in 2022 by:

Young Writers
Remus House
Coltsfoot Drive
Peterborough
PE2 9BF
Telephone: 01733 890066
Website: www.youngwriters.co.uk

Printed and bound in the UK by BookPrintingUK
Website: www.bookprintinguk.com
YB0490L

FOREWORD

For Young Writers' latest competition This Is Me,
we asked primary school pupils to look inside
themselves, to think about what makes them unique,
and then write a poem about it! They rose to the
challenge magnificently and the result is this fantastic
collection of poems in a variety of poetic styles.

Here at Young Writers our aim is to encourage creativity
in children and to inspire a love of the written word, so
it's great to get such an amazing response, with some
absolutely fantastic poems. It's important for children to
focus on and celebrate themselves and this competition
allowed them to write freely and honestly, celebrating
what makes them great, expressing their hopes and
fears, or simply writing about their favourite things.
This Is Me gave them the power of words. The result
is a collection of inspirational and moving poems that
also showcase their creativity and writing ability.

I'd like to congratulate all the young poets
in this anthology, I hope this inspires them
to continue with their creative writing.

CONTENTS

Thomas Holtrust (8)   60

Ladygrove Park Primary School, Didcot

Jacob Hathaway (10)	61
Ariana Whymark (10), James Spindler (11) & James Weeks (10)	62
Willow Vaughan-Jones (10)	63
Marie Streicher Eleuterio (10)	64
Isabella Thrupp (10)	65
Katie Vass (10)	66
Emily Douglas-Street (10)	67
Chloe Green (10)	68
Jennifer Williamson (10)	69
Matty Williams (11)	70
Izzy Smith (11)	71
Georgia Segal (10)	72
Aalaya Megha Anand (10)	73
Robert Richmond (10)	74
Rohan Talari (10)	75
Olivia Pratley (10)	76
Stribor Skoro (10)	77
Isaac Cliff (10)	78
Amelia Lake (10)	79
Erin Boniface (10)	80
Rosie Capper (11)	81
Gaia Militello (10)	82
Dylan Matthews (10)	83
Bella Merritt (10)	84
Imogen Webb (10)	85
Archie Nicholl (10)	86
Leah Jackson-Baah	87
Jack Stokes (10)	88
Anya Kachhela (10)	89
Maya Barber (10)	90
Sam Burbage (10)	91
Josh Larrett (10)	92
Jamie Smout (10)	93
Mia Coles (10)	94
Olivia Brenchley (10)	95
Sienna Davies (10)	96
Aarish Haval (10)	97

Little Hoole Primary School, Walmer Bridge

Sophia Williamson (10)	98
Kelsey-Rae Dunderdale (10)	100
Elizabeth Pilcher (11)	102
Imogen Cooper (10)	104
Tom Smith (10)	106
Alyssa Ridsdale (10)	108
Matthew Sutton (10)	110
Maisy Ackroyd (10)	112
Jack Griffiths (10)	114
Mia Greaves (11)	116
Dean Smith (10)	118
Halle Marcus (11)	120
Leo Holkham (10)	122
Harry Campbell (10)	124
George Cross (10)	126
Ray Watson (10)	128
Maisie Ingram (10)	130
Samuel Johnson (11)	132
Millie Hodgson (10)	134
Maisy Winder (11)	136

THE POEMS

When I Grow Up!

Everyone is different,
Including me,
And if you want to know more,
Read on and see.

I'm very competitive,
And think of everyone as my competition,
Serena Williams, Emma Radacanu,
They are my ambition.

When I grow up, I also want to be,
Someone who works with animals,
I'll do anything for dogs,
Like brushing them, feeding them and throwing
their balls.

Lilly Shepherd (9)
Downham CE (VC) Primary School, Ramsden Heath

Imperfect Me

No one's perfect,
Although I'd like to be!
So let me describe to you, my imperfect me!

I'm controlling and in charge like a giant stop sign,
Though I come back to say sorry, so I guess that
it's fine!
I never seem to care for my messy drawers,
Yet, now I see that it's one of my biggest flaws.

I'm impatient like a throbbing headache
And likely to crack and roar, "For goodness' sake!"
Boisterous and noisy at the crack of dawn,
But silent and sleepy when the curtains are drawn.

Burnt brownies and broken cookies galore,
Still, when it comes to improvements - I always
look for more,
Competitive and fierce with my eyes on number
one,
Though I come back down to Earth, cos' it's all
about the fun.

Noisy and messy and the other traits here,
It's all about being yourself, have no fear,
All the things I said are true,
So don't forget to be the imperfect you!

Isla Scott Evans (9)
Downham CE (VC) Primary School, Ramsden Heath

This Is Me

T oday I go to boxing and I do sparring in the ring
H ello I'm Casey
I like all types of animals some even say I like them too much
S ome people even say that I am sassy but kind

I have two super pretty Oreo-looking cats
S ome people say that I am sporty but I would not say that I am

M y friends say that I am trustworthy and talkative
E veryone says that my eyes are like glazed cocoa powder.

Casey Dryburgh (11)
Falla Hill Primary School, Fauldhouse

This Is Me!

I am funny and friendly
Smart and brave
As fast as a cheetah
Spelling is my superpower
But art makes me cower

I am as adventurous as a dog
I have crystal blue eyes
My favourite sport is football
But basketball makes me crawl

My favourite food is curry
I like to save my money
Most of the time I'm happy
But sometimes I am yappy

I'm as kind as a gran
And I am a major football fan
This is me.

Sam Donnelly (11)
Falla Hill Primary School, Fauldhouse

This Is Me!

T houghtful friend who is nice to all
H appy all the time and filled with excitement!
I nventing items with materials is fun
S uper at being responsible!

I ncludes everyone in our fun outdoor games
S easide is my favourite place to be!

M int green is my favourite colour because I like mint ice cream
E ncouraging others makes me happy

Litsa Eromokhodion (8)
Falla Hill Primary School, Fauldhouse

This Is Me

I am good at sports but football is the best
I make a darting run and leave the opposition in a mess.

I love my dog very much
He is so cute and always there when I am in a rush

I am very chatty, love to talk
and I love to go on walks

I am very active and love to go outdoors
Anything to avoid my chores

Now you can see that
This is me.

Beau Philp (11)
Falla Hill Primary School, Fauldhouse

This Is Me

T alkative, talented and trustworthy
H elpful house captain
I have a pretty perfect puppy called Bear
S ome things I like are my family, my puppy and my friends

I have big bright blue eyes
S ome people say I have pretty brown, blonde hair

M y friends describe me as loud and little
E xcellent, enthusiastic.

Grace Mason (10)
Falla Hill Primary School, Fauldhouse

This Is Me!

T iny in size,
H appy always but sometimes shy,
I love playing with my friends and my class!
S ometimes sad but always filled with delight!

I love learning spelling, maths and art is so much fun
S ummer is a merry and jolly time!

M y family, friends and teachers are all fun!
E verything is the best to me!

Leah Millar (8)

Falla Hill Primary School, Fauldhouse

Me

I am a...
Nice friend
Book reader
Chocolate eater
Tall
Helpful
Golf watcher
Dancer
Horse rider
Cheerleader
Boxer
Football watcher
Good friend
Strong
Thoughtful
Arty
Fearless
Rabbit lover
Horse lover
Quiet
Smart

Respectful
I have blonde hair
Blue eyes
And finally, friendly.

Sophie Smith (8)
Falla Hill Primary School, Fauldhouse

Me

I am...

A boxer
A rockstar
A joker
A good friend
Helpful
Kind

This is me!

Kye Babajide (8)
Falla Hill Primary School, Fauldhouse

This Is Me

I am a lightning bolt in football boots.
I am a rock in defence.
I am a lover of dogs, steak and spaghetti bolognese.
I am a lifelong football fan.
I am spectacularly sporty.
I am always active.
I am as quick and brave as a wolf.
My hair is like soaking sand.
My ocean eyes glimmer.
My calculator brain works like crazy.
This is me.

Dolan Carty (11)
Falla Hill Primary School, Fauldhouse

This Is Me

T raining for football is a blast
H elping to look after my dog
I ntelligent like Einstein
S itting on the couch, relaxing

I am a great goalkeeper for my football team
S tudying for school is hard

M aking pizza for dinner
E xceptionally fast like Usain Bolt!

David Dodds (10)
Falla Hill Primary School, Fauldhouse

This Is Me!

T he girl was born in august.

H air like pine wood.

I n the tiny forest.

S ome people call me quiet.

I 'm a dancing diva.

S ometimes I prance like a reindeer.

M y mum thinks I'm crazy.

E ven though I'm hard working and never lazy.

Megan Allen (11)

Falla Hill Primary School, Fauldhouse

Me

A kennings poem

I am a...
Music listener
Good at drawing
Nice person
Laptop monitor
Thoughtful person
Little reader
Peanut butter lover
Nice writer
A big softie (sometimes I like to cry)
Football watcher
Hungry eater (just ask my mum)
Cheerful person
And finally
A supportive friend.

Dana Reid (8)
Falla Hill Primary School, Fauldhouse

This Is Me

I am sweet I am kind
Depending on the time
Sometimes I make a fuss
But I know it's not that much

I am sporty I am smart
But my main power is art

I keep my family close because
I love them the most

I am bold and I am honest
I am tall as I am strongest
This is me!

Kayla Feeney (10)
Falla Hill Primary School, Fauldhouse

This Is Me

T houghtful I am
H appy as can be
I nspiring the younger that look up to me
S miley, smart and good at art

I am so kind and always find a time
S o sly yet ever so shy

M ean I am not, threat you shall not
E ver so polite, ever so kind.

Jo Hill (11)
Falla Hill Primary School, Fauldhouse

Me

A kennings poem

I am a...
Football watcher
A sport watcher
A runner
An annoying person (so my mum said!)
Football player
A midfielder
Funny
A healthy eater
A chatty person
A short person
A smart person
An animal lover
Green eyes
Light brown hair

This is me!

Cameron Hendry (9)
Falla Hill Primary School, Fauldhouse

This Is Me

T echnology and gaming is what I like to do
H anging out with my friends
I am a curious cat lover
S illy and fun

I am a creative coder
S mart and inventive

M aker of games
E xcellent artist.

Lee Duncan (11)

Falla Hill Primary School, Fauldhouse

This Is Me!

T all in size
H ot in summer
I like turtles
S illy with my friends

I am annoying (sometimes)
S now border when it snows

M ean when my brother upsets me
E nergetic when I play sports.

Tom McDougall (9)
Falla Hill Primary School, Fauldhouse

This Is Me!

T iny
H ave two hobbies
I am helpful
S easide is calm for me

I like to chill
S ea has calming sounds for me

M e and my friends have fun
E lephants' toothpaste is interesting.

Lucas Barr (8)
Falla Hill Primary School, Fauldhouse

This Is Me!

T idy is me (just as my mum!)
H ave video games
I love dogs
S eeing lots of movies

I eat sweets
S illy is me sometimes

M ake lots of new things
E than is my name!

Ethan Macfarlane (9)
Falla Hill Primary School, Fauldhouse

This Is Me!

T iny nose
H ave many friends
I love sleeping
S inger one day

I am annoying (sometimes)
S uper happy

M y favourite colour is purple
E nergetic always.

Olivia Lumsden (9)
Falla Hill Primary School, Fauldhouse

Me

I am a...
Football watcher
I am kind
I am a goalkeeper
I love food
I love spending time with family
I enjoy maths
I talk often
I like to play with my friends
I am supportive

This is me!

Mason Kerr (9)
Falla Hill Primary School, Fauldhouse

This Is Me!

T all in size
H ave fun
I am cool
S cotland supporter

I am funny
S trong

M e and my friends play Marco Polo
E gg is my favourite food.

Finlay D (8)
Falla Hill Primary School, Fauldhouse

Me

I am a...
Book reader
Fun to play with
Swimmer and compete in galas
Good friend
Love chocolate
Love games
PlayStation player
And finally
I am a good helper

This is me!

Lewis Coulter (9)
Falla Hill Primary School, Fauldhouse

Me

A kennings poem

I am a...
Snowboarder
Winter lover
Sweetie muncher
Football watcher
Pop-Tart lover
Pro gamer
Deep sleeper
And finally...
A cat lover

This is me!

Daniel Sutherland (9)

Falla Hill Primary School, Fauldhouse

Me

I am...
Funny
Good at basketball
Small
Kind
Fast
Strong
A good boxer
Smart
Blonde
Blue-eyed
Fast typer
Animal lover

This is me!

Callan Mcgonnal (9)

Falla Hill Primary School, Fauldhouse

Me

I am...

A kind person
A helpful person
Terrific
Good at drawing
Funny
Chatty
Special
And finally
I love my family

This is me!

Rebecca Delaney (9)
Falla Hill Primary School, Fauldhouse

Me

I am a...
Kind person
Helpful to my friends
A gamer
Fast
Energetic
Small
Joyful
A good friend
Emotional
Smart

This is me!

Aiden Bryans (9)
Falla Hill Primary School, Fauldhouse

Me

I am a ...
Drawer
Food fan
Tiny in size
Sweetie lover
Weird as can be
Winter wonderer
Halloween lover
Scotland fan

This is me!

Lola Daffurn (8)
Falla Hill Primary School, Fauldhouse

Me

A kennings poem

I am a...

Football player
Chocolate lover
Film watcher
Fruit eater
Caring person
I love my family

This is me!

Alfie McMeekin (8)
Falla Hill Primary School, Fauldhouse

This Is Me!

The girl who wrote this poem,
Loves dancing through the beach,
The sand glimmering like a golden peach.

She wouldn't mind some pasta,
And is stronger than a boar,
Her intelligence is hardcore,
And she's as curious as a cat,
Who's chasing a funny rat.

She knows languages of plenty,
And pink her colour is,
To ride across the rainbows,
Like a colour queen.

The girl who wrote this poem,
In copper pages, her life lies,
To books and all the reading,
She does when down she lies.

She likes playing under the big blue sky,
The trees as green as grass,

To hope that one day all that come,
Will joy and fun become.

The girl who wrote this poem,
Is pretty as a flower,
As bonny as a castle's tower.

She loves roaming through the forest,
Picking up the berries,
To only find out what on earth just made her so, so merry.

So now the time has come for you,
To find out who this is,
For all that has befallen her,
I tell this girl is me.

Camilla June (10)
InterHigh Education, Belfast

I Love Earth So Much

My garden is a supermarket, it grows everything.
I love its potatoes, carrots and every little thing.

My plants have names and characters too,
I take care of them as if I'm in a zoo!

My plants are alive and they give us life,
If I could marry them they would be my wife.

When I'm happy I garden and talk to the trees,
When I'm sad I walk through the green and all
through the leaves.

When I was little my nickname was potato,
And now that I'm seven my favourite food is
potato!

I love the earth so much and I love all its life.
Every day I watch nature change and I look for
beehives!

Everything about earth gives me so much joy.
I am so grateful for everything way more than any
toy!

Thank you life for this gift and thank you for InterHigh.
Because my awesome school has no roof I can still see the sky!

Valentine Zein Meyden (7)

InterHigh Education, Belfast

This Is Me

Hello, my name is Joana!
I am 12 years old and go to Interhigh School.
My favourite colour is blue
I love foxes because they're very cute.
My birthday is on the 9th of October which means
it was just recently!
It makes me happy when people are kind to me or
they defend me,
And I dislike it when people are rude to me even
though I didn't do anything or if they judge or
shame other people by who they are.
I would say what makes me, me is my sense of
humour,
Creativity, opinions on things, all that stuff.
My dream in the future is to own a pet,
Have my best friends as roommates,
And own a little cafe!

Joana Dinaro
InterHigh Education, Belfast

Of Course It's Me

Come here my fellows, let me tell you about a girl,
Who loves to draw, paint, dance and swirl,
She is as kind as her mum,
And she is friendly like a kitten,
Her cute little face is a blooming flower,
And she is as creative as cheeky pigeon,
Her favourite colour is pink, it is the sound of joys,
Because it always reminds her of her favourite
toys,
And while she can be clever and smart,
Just like a fox,
She is often too lazy,
Like a big slow sloth,
Can you make a guess now, who is she?
You don't need any hint, of course it's me!

Maryam Ahsan Amatul Rahman (7)
InterHigh Education, Belfast

Green

Green is everything - it is the whole Earth.
Green is the glorious nature surrounding us.
Green is a peaceful feeling running around the forest.
Green is a little sound waving through the wind.
Green is the scent of fresh mint in a salad.
Green is generous, it gives breathing air to us.
Green is everywhere!

Aydin Firoz Ashraf (7)
InterHigh Education, Belfast

All About Me

J oyful like a happy kid
A mazing, awesome and adventurous
S porty, strong and a superstar
M erry and marvellous
I ntelligent
N ice.

Jasmin Niculita (10)
Jesmond Gardens Primary School, Hartlepool

All About Me

C ool
A dventurous
I nventive
D efensive
E njoys sharing facts
N ice.

Caiden Jay Wilson (10)
Jesmond Gardens Primary School, Hartlepool

All About Me

D elightful

A dventurous

N ice

I nventive

E xcellent

L ikeable.

Daniel Shaw (9)

Jesmond Gardens Primary School, Hartlepool

All About Me

C ool
A rtistic
L ovely
L oyal
A mazing
N ice.

Callan Simpson (9)
Jesmond Gardens Primary School, Hartlepool

All About Me

C reative

H appy

L ikes the rain

O utgoing

E ntertaining.

Chloe Parkinson (9)
Jesmond Gardens Primary School, Hartlepool

All About Me

R ushes, runs and races
U nselfish
B rave
Y oung.

Ruby Liddle (8)

Jesmond Gardens Primary School, Hartlepool

All About Me

L ovely

E pic!

O utgoing

N ice.

Leon Foster (10)

Jesmond Gardens Primary School, Hartlepool

All About Me

S uper

H appy

A wesome

Y oung.

Shay Malham (7)

Jesmond Gardens Primary School, Hartlepool

This Is Me...

I am a daisy blooming in the green grass.

I am a fierce lion with teeth as sharp as scissors.

I am an hourglass, time ticking with sand falling to its doom, waiting to be tipped over, *tick, tick, tick.*

I am a mirror falling,
shards of a spider's web causing seven years of bad luck.

I am an eye gazing into someone's soul,
looking if they are passionate about their world.

I am a chalkboard, write on me all you want,
I will swallow the secrets.

This is me.

Billie Hazelton (10)
Kinlochleven Primary School, Kinlochleven

I Am

I am a sponge at the bottom of the sea,
as soggy as a wetsuit after five hours of swimming.

I am a knight, riding on a blazing ball of fire,
my armour is melting.

I am a wizard, flying high in the sky with the
clouds,
a lizard deep in the dark and cold woods.

I am a shadow, lost high in the sky at night, by the
moonlight.
A soul lost underground,
cold like ice, dark like black.

I am a ball of fire in the deep water,
burning out like an old candle.

I am a giant in a small world.
I am lonely; I miss all my giant friends.
Blocks of ice in the desert slowly melting, it is hot.

I am a grain of sand on the moon,
cold and alone looking down at the earth.

I miss you!

I am a wave of lava in the deep and cold water at night.
An apple bobbing in the dark.
A melting snowball in the hot summer.

I am a clock going back in time,
Whooshing and whirling.

I am a dark cloud in the middle of a hot summer,
I block the sun all day.

I am me.

Kyle McNulty (10)
Kinlochleven Primary School, Kinlochleven

I Am

I am a school teaching all the kids.
Subtraction, similes, spelling.

I am a keyboard typing all over me.
Tap, tap, and tap.

I am a bag carrying secrets everywhere.
Hidden in a magic lamp.

I am the sun shining through all of the neighbour's windows.
Reflections everywhere.

I am rubber, swishing all over the paper,
Swipe, swipe, swipe.

I am a tray filled with lots of colourful pens and pencils.
Pink, blue and purple like a rainbow.

This is me.

Lana Lindsay (9)
Kinlochleven Primary School, Kinlochleven

I Am

I am
I am a rock as hard as the earth in a fire.
I am a tiger, my eyes filled with fire and rage hunting down my prey.
I am a nebula, as beautiful as a sunset on the beach.
I am the big bang; I came from nothing to something, one of the biggest mysteries in the world.
I am an asteroid, with a goal to destroy life.
I am a book where anything is possible from fairy tales to thrillers.

Shay Lindsay (11)
Kinlochleven Primary School, Kinlochleven

This Is Me!

This is me!
I am an eye looking into a bright soul,
hidden in my chest.

I am a tray,
eating anything people put in me.

I am a lion,
that would eat everything to lose hunger.

I am a sword,
that can cut through anything on this planet.

I am a powerful orb,
that holds so much energy.

I am a God,
that made the world.

I am me.

Dominic Pelyhe (9)
Kinlochleven Primary School, Kinlochleven

I Am

I am a mirror that reflects a shadow
in a windy valley.

I am a rose that blooms in the daylight,
with a black tint.

I am a cat lost in a forest,
in the moonlight.

I am a star looking down on the world.

I am a pen,
I write about the past, the present and the future.

I am a planet glowing,
waiting to be found

I am me.

Freya Nicolson (10)
Kinlochleven Primary School, Kinlochleven

I Am...

I am an enormous grenade about to
explode into the sunlight

I am a spinning jet
flying into battle
swoosh

I am a burly soldier
fighting for my life

I am a speeding bullet
aiming for my prey

I am a secret base
hiding in the flames.

I am a bulletproof chest plate
saving soldiers

This is me.

Amber Martin (9)
Kinlochleven Primary School, Kinlochleven

I Am

I am a notebook with clean, smooth, white sheets
of paper
hiding from the people who want to draw and
write in me.
I am a shiny green emerald thirty-five feet
underground waiting to be found.
I am a pink axolotl gliding gracefully through the
turquoise water of the Mediterranean.
This is me.

Ethan Doogan (10)
Kinlochleven Primary School, Kinlochleven

This Is Me

I am a bin filled with dark secrets,
Safe and hidden at the bottom of the world.

I am a pancake filled with lies,
Guilt hugging the soul tightly.

I am a banana drenched in happiness.
Swirly and sticky.

This is me.

Euan Allen (10)
Kinlochleven Primary School, Kinlochleven

This Is Me!

I am a snow-covered mountain,
crunchy ice below my feet.

I am an abandoned well,
no coins just darkness.

I am an ice cave,
black as the night.

I am the big grey man of Ben Macdhui,
I am me.

Dewar Nicolson (10)
Kinlochleven Primary School, Kinlochleven

Thomas

T errifically fun
H elpful and kind
O range is my favourite colour
M arshmallows are my favourite food
A mazing
S illy.

Thomas Holtrust (8)
Kinlochleven Primary School, Kinlochleven

Space Is Me

The cosmic universe is a lot of fun.
The stars up above Earth down below.
We will fly past the moon and say goodbye to
Earth.
I want to live in outer space,
Where stars are out to chase
We've got moons, comets across the world,
We've got the whole universe out here and more.
Stars up above Earth down below.
We'll fly past the moon and say goodbye to Earth.
I want to live in outer space,
Where the stars are out to chase
We got moons, comets across the world
We got the whole universe out here and more.

Jacob Hathaway (10)
Ladygrove Park Primary School, Didcot

This Is Me

I am a dyslexic Bob Ross
I'm a high scoring gamer
I'm a brilliant boxer on a pogo stick
I hate olives - green ones are the worst
I dislike tomatoes - the taste makes me sick!
Tennis is the sport I love
Whacking balls at 100 miles per hour removes my anger
A chocolate and steak-loving mad child
For breakfast that's the best!
Halloween pumpkins - I don't know
The smell is quite disgusting but makes great pie
Simba, Nala, Eysha, Poppy and Crombie -
Licky, energetic, crazy dogs.

Ariana Whymark (10), James Spindler (11) & James Weeks (10)
Ladygrove Park Primary School, Didcot

This Is Willow

T his is me
H appiness is fun
I like to go on dog walks
S he has stupendous talks with her teacher

I love to have a little nap
S he loves to slap

W hat she doesn't know is she's great at singing
I love to dance as well
L ove, life, laughter
L eah is her best friend
O range is her least favourite colour
W illow is her name.

Willow Vaughan-Jones (10)
Ladygrove Park Primary School, Didcot

This Is Me

This is me
I'm a sleeping machine
I don't really like tea
My friends know I'm not mean
Cats and dogs are super cute
Video games are the best
Sometimes my friends want to put me on mute
I feel relieved after a maths test
I do piano on Mondays and drama on Fridays
But the best day of all is the 18th of May!
Yay!
This is who I am
It's who I'll always be
Goodbye for now
This is me.

Marie Streicher Eleuterio (10)
Ladygrove Park Primary School, Didcot

This Is Me

I am a brilliant gymnast
I am a fantastic baker
I am a Roblox lover
I love to do flips and tricks
I love animals, but puppies are my favourite
When I'm bored, I always play with my brother
My favourite school subjects are art and
computing
When I grow up I want to be an Olympic gymnast
My favourite food is candyfloss, it's like a cloud in
your mouth that just melts away
This is me!

Isabella Thrupp (10)
Ladygrove Park Primary School, Didcot

This Is Me

Who plays Roblox 24/7,
Has a pet dog called Max?
Who is a major wizarding world fan?
Harry Potter is the best.
Whose favourite TV show is Friends
And knows the names by heart?
Who would eat a whole pizza
As long as there's less cheese?
Who would eat a lifetime's supply of chocolate
And still want more?
Who is as tall as a giraffe?
The answer is me!
Of course it is, who else?

Katie Vass (10)
Ladygrove Park Primary School, Didcot

This Is Me Emily

T alented in gymnastics
H appy like my dog Alfie
I ncredible at making things tidy
S corpio that is me

I like chocolate but the thing I like is hot chocolate with cream because it's the best
S ome books I like the best are adventures with a twist

M y one dislike is an untidy mess
E mily is my name and this is me.

Emily Douglas-Street (10)
Ladygrove Park Primary School, Didcot

Now You Know

Reading in the library
Reading in the park
I have a fluffy dog who likes to bark
Having two rabbits, Honey and Daisy
Helps not to be lazy
I love painting
Sports is fun too
I'm clumsy
I love music
I love chocolate
What about you?
Camping on the mountains
Walking on the beach
I love writing
This is me!

Chloe Green (10)
Ladygrove Park Primary School, Didcot

Inside My Mind

I am an artist holding a pen
Sometimes I am as silly as a hen
I am a dark monster lover playing basketball
Animal lover, I love them all
Social media star I sometimes think
Binge watcher I do not blink
Best friend I really am
Half Egyptian you know it fam
I have a good eye for fashion
Bad thoughts I bash 'em
This is me.

Jennifer Williamson (10)
Ladygrove Park Primary School, Didcot

Me: Matty

Science is very fun.
A ton of pasta makes me go yum.
Cycling's my favourite sport.
I'll be an inventor I also thought.
Super space
Is my favourite place.
Getting there is not a piece of cake.
I'm never late
For school; I can also wait
Longer than most. I sometimes dream,
I'm never mean.
This is me.

Matty Williams (11)
Ladygrove Park Primary School, Didcot

A Recipe For Me

A dash of sugar making everything sweet,
A sprinkle of messiness, not too neat,
A cup of chattiness,
A drizzle of happiness,
Now you know how to make half of me!
Add a lump of drawing,
Art theory is boring,
Add a chunk of writing,
Now make it exciting,
A bit of music,
Let me choose it,
Now you've made me!

Izzy Smith (11)
Ladygrove Park Primary School, Didcot

How To Make Me

You will need:
A book-filled bedroom
A dollop of chocolate
10lbs of love
1000g of kindness
Now
Mix together with love and kindness
Then
Add a dollop of chocolate
Mix it in a book-filled bedroom
Then put in the oven to boil and bubble
Take out to cool
Sprinkle me with beach sand and sea
This is me.

Georgia Segal (10)
Ladygrove Park Primary School, Didcot

This Is Me

I am a lightning bolt with a racquet,
Playing with the different chords.
A determined figure in a jacket,
Sometimes acting like the master of swords.

Fast to furious, normal to fame,
Peace in the world is all I see.
Rapid Reader is my name,
'Cause I can be whatever I want to be -
This is me!

Aalaya Megha Anand (10)
Ladygrove Park Primary School, Didcot

This Is Me

My name is Robert
Good at football
Don't like maths
Cracked at Fortnite
Don't like Arsenal
But like Tottenham
My favourite animal is a crocodile
I like playing Fortnite with James, Jack, Tommy and Noah
Sometimes I wish I could sleep all day
My dream is to be a professional footballer.

Robert Richmond (10)
Ladygrove Park Primary School, Didcot

About Myself

A good cricketer
B rave badminton player
O utrageous as a lion
U nique person
T echy person

M etaphorical monster
Y earning reader
S pectacular scene
E ngulf sometimes
L oving creatures
F an favourite.

Rohan Talari (10)

Ladygrove Park Primary School, Didcot

This Is Me

My name is Olivia
I am a brilliant artist
I love my dog
She is a Miniature Schnauzer
She fights like a kick-boxer
(By the way I love kick-boxing too)
She is my softest teddy,
Other than my bunny teddy,
I have had since I was a baby
I love to cuddle her and play Roblox.

Olivia Pratley (10)
Ladygrove Park Primary School, Didcot

This Is Me

S cience is fun

T echnology is exciting

R eading has its ups and downs

I do not like how Indian food looks like

B iology is a hobby (well, watching biology documentaries)

O blong is fun to say

R hyming and poetry are not my thing.

Stribor Skoro (10)

Ladygrove Park Primary School, Didcot

I Am...

I am...
A brilliant baker
A terrific typer
An amazing athletic ape
A cool camping creator
A fast food flipper
An awesome adorable animal lover
A slow snoring sleeper
A glorious gifting gamer
An absolutely amazing artist
A technical taekwondo thinker.

Isaac Cliff (10)
Ladygrove Park Primary School, Didcot

Me

Cooking is my thing
Taekwondo is my strength
Halloween is my fright
Holidays are my light
Comfort is my safety
Playing is my life
Cinema is my screen
McDonald's is my food
Minecraft is my game
Scooter is my fun
Football is my goal.

Amelia Lake (10)
Ladygrove Park Primary School, Didcot

Friends

F unny, always there for you
R eaders of minds always know your feelings
I s a helping hand
E nergetic always sees the best in you
N othing more than amazing
D on't be afraid just
S peak to a friend.

Erin Boniface (10)
Ladygrove Park Primary School, Didcot

Easter

E njoy chocolate with friends
A fter dinner eat chocolate
S teal other people's chocolate
T hank the Easter Bunny
E at more chocolate
R ead the wrappers to see how much sugar you devoured.

Rosie Capper (11)

Ladygrove Park Primary School, Didcot

This Is Me

T he Hobbit film lover
H appy as a panda
I am a Roblox gamer
S ometimes angry (rarely)

I am a karate champion
S ometimes sad

M ostly kind
E xciting.

Gaia Militello (10)

Ladygrove Park Primary School, Didcot

Me

A kennings poem

I am a
Great gamer
Swimming superstar
Badminton boss
Helping human
Kind crab
Hiking hybrid
Mathematical genius
Articulate artist
Fine footballer
And can't forget
A smart student.

Dylan Matthews (10)
Ladygrove Park Primary School, Didcot

All About Me

Hello
I like to swim, run and do something fun
My friends say I'm funny, kind and sort of smart
But I know this poem comes from the heart
I would eat a midnight feast
I don't live in the Middle East.

Bella Merritt (10)
Ladygrove Park Primary School, Didcot

This Is Me

A kennings poem

This is me,
Sweet demolisher
Animal lover
Happy helper
Humorous roasts
Funny friend
Curious carer
Cricket player
This is me and who I am
I am fine being me
This is who I wanna be.

Imogen Webb (10)
Ladygrove Park Primary School, Didcot

Football Is Great

F antastic football
O utrageous players
O ptimum people
T errific length of pitch
B est goals
A thletic athletes
L egendary lines
L uxury legs.

Archie Nicholl (10)
Ladygrove Park Primary School, Didcot

This Is Me, Leah

My name is Leah
I'm a girl who goes to school,
I'm kind, caring, loving.
I'm a good helping hand
I think I am funny like a bunny
So when you're sad,
Come to me.

Leah Jackson-Baah
Ladygrove Park Primary School, Didcot

This Is Me

I like football and playing games
I like burgers
I play FIFA 21 with Noah (who is my friend)
I play Fortnite with Kacper, Noah and Robert
I like Netflix
But don't like school.

Jack Stokes (10)
Ladygrove Park Primary School, Didcot

This Is Who I Am

A nya is who I am

N o wait, I love drawing

Y ou and me could be similar for my sports I play, sleeping I am good at

A rt I like, dancing, singing and dogs.

Anya Kachhela (10)

Ladygrove Park Primary School, Didcot

Dance

D ance makes me happy
A t dance we have fun
N ever giving up
C uz in dance you need to believe
E veryone can do dance as long as they believe.

Maya Barber (10)
Ladygrove Park Primary School, Didcot

Strategic Pigeon

Haiku poetry

I am a soaring
pigeon, strategic, goofy
I write and I draw

I'm annoying but
I can focus, simply be
Cautious, this is me.

Sam Burbage (10)
Ladygrove Park Primary School, Didcot

It's My Name

J osh is good at games
O h why are you not happy?
S o hi, what's your name?
H ow are you so good at this game?

Josh Larrett (10)

Ladygrove Park Primary School, Didcot

Me

I am a fantastic drawer
I love all animals
But fish are my favourite
I get angry and sad
But mostly happy
This is me.

Jamie Smout (10)

Ladygrove Park Primary School, Didcot

This Is Me!

A kennings poem

I am a...
Super baller
Speedy runner
Quick eater
Goal scorer
Fast footballer
Goal assister
Good defender.

Mia Coles (10)

Ladygrove Park Primary School, Didcot

Water

O cean

L ight a candle

I sle of white beach

V alley

I ce melts

A pples red.

Olivia Brenchley (10)

Ladygrove Park Primary School, Didcot

Bendy Spider

A kennings poem

I am a...
Flexible gymnast
Family lover
Egg hater
Competition striker
Harry Potter reader
Bendy spider.

Sienna Davies (10)
Ladygrove Park Primary School, Didcot

This Is Me

A kennings poem

I am a...
High helicopter
Playful person
Constructive builder
Colossal fan
This is me.

Aarish Haval (10)
Ladygrove Park Primary School, Didcot

This Is Me

Sophia, Sophia, never let me have much sugar,
I am as sweet as anything, like to play little games
of snooker.
Cheeky girl, I tell little fibs,
I cherish food, especially ribs.

Sympathetic soul, intrepid brain
Glamourous magenta cheeks, mind as tough as
chains.
Distinguished smile impossible to draw a blank,
Everybody gives me a thank you.

Hyperactive eyes, enchanting heart,
Art is my passion, I am quite smart.
Kicking, scoring football is my game,
Everyone knows that Pocket Rocket's my name.

Incredible, incomparable dancing moves,
Athletic legs, If you need I will prove.
Argumentatively talking, will I get told off?
Dodging and ducking ready for take-off.

Sophia, Sophia, never let me have much sugar,
I am as sweet as anything, like to play little games
of snooker.
Cheeky girl, I tell little fibs,
I cherish food, especially ribs.

Sophia Williamson (10)
Little Hoole Primary School, Walmer Bridge

This Is Me

Kelsey-Rae, Kelsey-Rae, a delightful soul,
Such a good girl for Christmas, I never get coal,
Always working hard and trying my best,
Guinea pigs and dogs, I am obsessed.

Ruby-red lips, wavy, honey hair,
Humorous person, always trying to scare,
Charcoal-black eyelashes, thousands of unique
freckles,
Diamond, sapphire eyes, like glittery speckles.

Hard-working person, mature mind,
Impatient brain, very kind,
Encouraging heart, funny humour,
Proud of myself and never spreading a rumour.

Kicking a football, ducking and diving,
Running on the pitch, sweating and panting,
Pacing around the bowling green,
Boxing the punch bag, living the dream.

Kelsey-Rae, Kelsey-Rae, a delightful soul,
Such a good girl... for Christmas, I never get coal,
Always working hard and trying my best,
Guinea pigs and dogs, I am obsessed.

Kelsey-Rae Dunderdale (10)

Little Hoole Primary School, Walmer Bridge

This Is Me

Elizabeth, Elizabeth, no sense of humour
Likes lots of games, doesn't believe any rumours
Whilst playing snooker, as silent as a boulder
Will I be like this when I'm older?

Sapphire eyes, bronze, short hair
When it comes to presents, I don't share
Creased, untidy clothes and tanned skin
But who am I really within?

Am I athletic with a sporty body?
Because I like football as a hobby
I really like gaming with my friends
Because whilst I'm doing it the fun never ends

In class my brain is nifty
But outside I'm playing swiftly
Running rapidly, I'm on the path
Another thing I'm quick at is maths

Elizabeth, Elizabeth, bad sense of humour,
Likes lots of games, doesn't believe any rumours.

In snooker as strong as a boulder
What will I be like when I'm older?
This is me.

Elizabeth Pilcher (11)
Little Hoole Primary School, Walmer Bridge

This Is Me

Imogen, Imogen an equestrian at sight
Got to make sure the girth is put up tight
What will happen in my future?
Where will God take me in life?

Charcoal black eyelashes, deep brown button eyes
Thick tangled hair oh what a surprise
A cheerful white face, welcoming and calm
A medium-sized girl who lives on a farm

Small strong legs, prefer to stay still
Medium-sized feet, I don't have much skill
Good core strength, I never slack
You've got to admit I'm a horse riding maniac

I can be quite bossy, but not all the time
If something's out of place it becomes a crime
I'm careful and kind, like to help out
I get bored easily, I am not normally loud

Imogen, Imogen an equestrian at sight
Got to make sure the girth is put up tight
What will happen in the future?
Where will God take me in life?

Imogen Cooper (10)
Little Hoole Primary School, Walmer Bridge

This Is Me

Tom, Tom
Running and kicking a football is my game
Xbox and YouTube, Smith is my nickname
A good-humoured sister and a dog called Bettie
A caring heart, I am very friendly

Ice white hair, an excellent brain
Midnight-blue eyes, legs immune to pain
Sticky out ears, olive skin
A little bit tall and also quite slim

When I am running I am guaranteed to fall
Grip tech hands, exceptional for basketball
Athletic legs, outstanding speed
When I am playing I have to succeed

Helpful soul, enchanting heart
Besides the fractions, I am quite smart
A fearless boy with an inquisitive mind
Always ready and really kind

Tom, Tom
Running, kicking a football is my game
Xbox and YouTube, Smith is my nickname
A good-humoured sister and a dog called Bettie
A caring heart and I am very friendly.

Tom Smith (10)
Little Hoole Primary School, Walmer Bridge

This Is Me

Alyssa, Alyssa as quiet as a mouse,
Constantly at my friend's house.
No matter what I'll always try,
When I'm at school I'm really shy.

Golden like hair, navy-blue eyes,
A sneaky little girl who always lies.
Long like nails, thin little nose,
Flaming freckles, heart like a rose.

Sporty long legs, flexible spine,
I don't even think it is in line.
Learning very quickly, intrepid mind,
When I'm running I'm never behind.

Terrible jokes, heart like a pot of gold,
When I'm outside I'm always cold.
Talking constantly kind like heart,
When I'm with my friends we can't get apart.

Alyssa, Alyssa as quiet as a mouse,
Constantly at my friend's house,
No matter what I'll always try,
When I'm at school I'm really shy.

Alyssa Ridsdale (10)
Little Hoole Primary School, Walmer Bridge

This Is Me

Matthew, Matthew is a friendly chap
Favourite colour is blue always got a trick under
my cap
Will I be a successful chap?
Could I be a comedian and make everyone clap?

Long powerful legs, peacock-blue eyes
Pineapple like eyebrows I think my mind is wise
Hair as brown as gingerbread
Tawny coloured freckles on my nose

Trustworthy soul with a creative mind
Make me angry, my teeth will grind
Adventurously curious, very friendly chap
A polite heart, don't want to have a scrap

Running fast, striding steps
Arms up high squishy biceps
Football is my favourite game
When I'm older will I have fame?

Matthew, Matthew is a friendly chap
Favourite colour is blue always got a trick under my cap
Will I be a successful chap?
Could I be a comedian and make everyone clap?

Matthew Sutton (10)
Little Hoole Primary School, Walmer Bridge

This Is Me

This is me
Maisy, Maisy, always loud
When I play football I'm proud
Do you think I'll ever be famous?
I play outside with no darkness

Blush-like cheeks, caramel-brown eyes
Big monkey ears, a sneaky little girl telling lies
Small freckled nose a cheeky little grin
Teeth white as paper tanned clear skin

Calm as a library, clapping like a seal
Always waiting for my next meal
Like and love to travel to Turkey
My sister is like a crazy monkey

Hairy legs like a gorilla
Have a warm heart it's like a protective umbrella
When my shoe size doesn't fit, I order the next
shoe size
When I play football, I wish for a prize

Maisy, Maisy, always loud
When I play football I'm proud
Do you think I'll be famous?
I play outside with no darkness.

Maisy Ackroyd (10)
Little Hoole Primary School, Walmer Bridge

This Is Me

Jack, Jack that's the name
Loves sport especially the footy game
Wants to play for Leicester City
People think I'm small what a pity.

Chubby round head, soft pale skin
Tiny square nose, super slim
Yellow stained teeth, short ginger hair
Walnut eyes, a mighty stare.

As fast as a lightning bolt, springs in my feet
Explosive punches, a deadly defeat
Sensational football skills, kick like a cow
Dangerously bad dance moves, an exquisite bow

Bizarre thoughts, quirky odd mind
Enchanting heart, really kind
Never stops, always sporty
Annoy my sister, very naughty.

Jack, Jack that's the name
Loves sport especially the footy game
Wants to play for Leicester city
People think I'm small, what a pity.

Jack Griffiths (10)
Little Hoole Primary School, Walmer Bridge

This Is Me

Mia, Mia, I have a fear
Little moons are yummy, when I laugh I sneer
I am quiet, sometimes I'm not
I like wearing pink, I don't like being apart

Long blonde hair, flamingo-pink lips
I have a girly style, I have middle age hips
One single freckle, diamond blue eyes
Sea-green glasses, I have a high shoe size

Running wild, pacing quickly
Hip swaying, strutting sassily
Falling over, stumbling constantly
Running fast, racing rapidly

Funny sounds, rusty car noise
Loving school, hard-working
Kind person, warm heart
Long hikes, adventurous thoughts

Mia, Mia, I have a fear
Little moons are yummy, when I laugh I sneer
I am quiet, sometimes I'm not
I like wearing pink, I do not like being apart.

Mia Greaves (11)

Little Hoole Primary School, Walmer Bridge

This Is Me!

Dean, Dean is a gleeful guy
No matter the challenge I always try
Whatever time, whatever weather
The next day I will always be better.

Tanned skin, Aegean eyes
Scruffy blonde hair, truly wise
Stick arms and bruised legs
Cheeky scarred face not by eggs.

Clumsy hands, intrepid mind
Cautiously calm, really kind
Trusting, athletic wouldn't lie
Anti-sociable but not a super-secret spy.

Sliding, rolling an extremely solid punch
Powerful strides to get to my colossal lunch
Wandering around, darting at speed
Scoring outrageous goals, aiming to succeed.

Dean, Dean is a gleeful guy
No matter the challenge I will always try
Whatever the time whatever the weather
The next day will always be better.

Dean Smith (10)
Little Hoole Primary School, Walmer Bridge

This Is Me

Halle, Halle, an annoying child,
Sometimes you will think I'm wild,
Always on my games at home,
Never out my bed so I don't roam!

Lightly freckled cheeks, deep-brown eyes
I might have a mind of lies,
Blush-pink lips, chocolate-brown hair,
With a face ever so fair.

A loving heart, loud voice,
When I'm older what will be my choice?
Heart of gold, impatient mind,
I'm sure I'm ever so kind.

Slowly running, irksomely talking,
When I'm nice to my sister I'm just acting
Skipping dumbly, smiling widely,
Almost always moving so happily!

Halle, Halle, an annoying child,
Sometimes you will think I'm wild,
Always on my games at home,
Never out my bed so I don't roam!

Halle Marcus (11)

Little Hoole Primary School, Walmer Bridge

This Is Me

Leo, Leo as smart as can be
My favourite sport is rugby
My favourite console is Xbox
I like to trap my sister in a box

Jaunty spots, hazel eyes
Large ears, kindly compromise
Reassuring smile, cocoa hair
Long eyelashes, I rarely care

Very funny, significantly polite
I like giving my brother a fright
Rather intelligent, confident voice
Immensely talented, I make a lot of noise.

Sensational scrum, rugby is my game
Fake passing, they call me the flame
It can be painful but it's always fun
Slow but strong, the best celebration is when we
won.

Leo, Leo as smart as can be
My favourite sport is rugby
My favourite console is Xbox
I like to trap my sister in a box.

Leo Holkham (10)
Little Hoole Primary School, Walmer Bridge

This Is Me

Harry, Harry, the friendly kid
Mostly nice, never hate
Always outside playing football
Maybe I'll become the best in the world

Thousands of freckles, intrepid mind
Short, ginger hair and I am kind
Golden heart, a brave brain
If I have too much sugar, I'll go insane

Athletic legs, lightning speed
If I play a game I have to succeed
Funky laugh, talk too much
Filled with energy always in a rush

Humorous soul, very creative
Cheeky boy, always active
I am me, forever will be
Never change, annoyingly crazy

Harry, Harry the friendly kid
Mostly nice never hate
Always outside playing football
Maybe I'll become the best in the world.

Harry Campbell (10)

Little Hoole Primary School, Walmer Bridge

This Is Me

George, George a lively body,
Who dared friend this monstrosity?
Funny friend, cheeky child,
Here I am, running wild.

Russet-brown hair, emerald eyes,
Marvellous mole, mind of lies,
Acute ears, cuts on my knees,
Rapid legs, run with ease.

Exquisite reflexes, rampaging runner,
Accurate eyes, winning jumper,
Annoying my sister, sudden run,
Charging at her with a Nerf gun!

Clumsy hands, terrible jokes,
Enjoys sports, getting soaked,
Backhand like a pro, passion for tennis,
Appreciates football, my energy is endless!

George, George a lively body,
Who dares friend this monstrosity?
Funny friend, cheeky child,
Here I am, running wild.

George Cross (10)

Little Hoole Primary School, Walmer Bridge

This Is Me

Light brown hair, navy blue eyes
Dark brown freckles like a spy.
Long eyelashes, small freckle nose
Short brown hair I suppose.

Small tiny freckles, short brown hair
Gigantic blue eyes, it is very rare
Freckled face, strong heart
Small lips, terrible at art.

Running rapidly, like a tiger
Loves games, hates spiders.
Never mean, always nice
Likes school, loves spice.

Very fast, rugby I like
Walks slowly I dislike
Doesn't like football, I'm very bad
Likes rugby I get mad.

Light brown hair, navy blue eyes
Dark brown freckles like a spy
Long eyelashes small freckle nose
Short brown hair I suppose.

Ray Watson (10)

Little Hoole Primary School, Walmer Bridge

This Is Me

Maisie, Maisie very lazy
And I'm very crazy,
Funny person mischievous child
Here I am going wild.

Pink, coral cheeks, curly brown hair
Flamingo-pink lips, heart full of care
Light peach skin, sea-blue eyes
Pearly white teeth, not very wise.

Impatient brain, lovely mind
Energetic body, very kind
Full of care, cheerful heart
Really friendly, loves art.

Dancing powerfully, crossing my feet
Hitting my brother with defeat
Skipping rapidly, jumping very crazy
Sometimes really lazy.

Maisie, Maisie very lazy
And I'm very crazy
Funny person mischievous child
Here I am, running wild.

Maisie Ingram (10)
Little Hoole Primary School, Walmer Bridge

This Is Me

Sam, Sam is super small
Likes to call and likes to brawl
Likes to game, likes to eat
And very big feet.

Wonky teeth, chocolate eyes
Cream peach skin creates lots of lies.
Round nose, walnut- brown hair
Big feet and plays fair.

A booming voice, a brave heart
Likes to swing on the shopping cart
Intrepid mind, creative brain
Likes to game and travel to Spain.

Springy step, likes to eat Greggs
Nonchalantly walking athletic legs
Super funny super smile
Crazy kid, crazy style.

Sam, Sam is super small
Likes to call and likes to brawl
Likes to game likes to eat
And very big feet.

Samuel Johnson (11)

Little Hoole Primary School, Walmer Bridge

This Is Me

Millie, Millie quiet as a mouse,
And loves cows.
Has perfect brows,
And a massive growl.

Flamingo flamed lips,
Long fingertips.
And a very strong grip,
When I walk I usually trip.

Body extremely flexible,
I'm mostly sensible.
My favourite colour is blue,
Everything I say is normally true.

Independent mind,
Loving heart.
I'm always smart,
I love art, I'm always a sweetheart.

Millie, Millie quiet as a mouse,
And loves cows.
Has perfect brows,
And one massive growl.

Millie Hodgson (10)
Little Hoole Primary School, Walmer Bridge

This Is Me

Maisy, Maisy is a daisy
Not lazy very crazy
Whatever the weather
I am better?

Pink glossy lip, poison green eyes
Tiny feet brain of lie
Tiny legs blond hair
Pearl blue glasses people glare

Running slowly skipping
Jump up down walking quickly
Not good at swimming good dances
I got the fourth change

Very shy very nice
Very dumb tell lies
Very loving gold heart
Not very smart

Maisy, Maisy is a daisy
Not lazy very crazy
Whatever the weather
Am I better?

Maisy Winder (11)

Little Hoole Primary School, Walmer Bridge

YOUNG WRITERS INFORMATION

We hope you have enjoyed reading this book – and that you will continue to in the coming years.

If you're the parent or family member of an enthusiastic poet or story writer, do visit our website **www.youngwriters.co.uk/subscribe** and sign up to receive news, competitions, writing challenges and tips, activities and much, much more! There's lots to keep budding writers motivated!

If you would like to order further copies of this book, or any of our other titles, then please give us a call or order via your online account.

Young Writers
Remus House
Coltsfoot Drive
Peterborough
PE2 9BF
(01733) 890066
info@youngwriters.co.uk

Join in the conversation!
Tips, news, giveaways and much more!

 YoungWritersUK YoungWritersCW youngwriterscw